The Royal Dinner

Written by Brenda Parkes
Illustrated by John Burge

GW00776312

The King told the cook,
"I want ham for my dinner,
ham for my dinner or it's
OFF WITH YOUR HEAD!"

2

The Queen told the cook,
"I want cheese for my dinner,
cheese for my dinner or it's
OFF WITH YOUR HEAD!"

3

The Prince told the cook,
"I want tomato for my dinner,
tomato for my dinner or it's
OFF WITH YOUR HEAD!"

The Princess told the cook,
"I want onion for my dinner,
onion for my dinner or it's
OFF WITH YOUR HEAD!"

The cook told the kitchen boys,
"They *all* want something different!
They *all* want something different
or it's OFF WITH MY HEAD!"

So he puzzled
and he
pondered.

He looked
and he read.

101 DISHES
FIT FOR
A KING

Royal
Recipes

1 Lump of Pastry
2 Cups of Ham
3 Cups of Cheese
2 Tomatoes
1 Large Onion

Then he found the perfect recipe. "This is it!" he said.

So he stirred
and he rolled

and he peeled
and he sliced.

He chipped
and he chopped

and he grated
and he diced.

He put it in the oven.
Then he mopped his brow and said,
"I hope they all like it or it's
OFF WITH MY HEAD!"

The cook told the King,
"I have a dish to please.
It has ham, tomato, onion,
and the Queen's special cheese."

10

"We hope we all like it,"
the royal family said.

"We hope we all like it or it's
OFF WITH YOUR HEAD!"

"Mmm,"
said the King.
"It tastes delicious!"

"Mmm,"
said the Queen.
"It tastes nutritious."

The Prince and the Princess said,
"This is just right!"

And they ate that pizza
to the very last bite.

In came the cook.
"Is it OFF WITH MY HEAD?"
"No," they all shouted.

15

"We'll crown you instead!"